Strange Stories from

Electrical Experimenter Magazine

Unusual articles gleaned
from early issues of
Electrical Experimenter
Magazine, 1917-1919

reprinted by Lindsay Publications Inc

Strange Stories from

Electrical Experimenter Magazine

Originally published by
Electrical Experimenter Magazine
New York

Original copyright 1917-1919
by E. P. Co. Inc
New York

Reprinted by
Lindsay Publications Inc
Bradley IL 60915

ISBN 1-55918-161-3

1 2 3 4 5 6 7 8 9 0

1995

CONTENTS

Gravitation and Electricity
5

Can Electricity Destroy Gravitation?
6

A Novel Tesla Steam Electric Clock
11

The Electrical Production of Synthetic Gasoline
13

Tesla's Egg of Columbus
18

My Inventions;
The Discovery of the Tesla Coil and Transformer
25

The Thought Recorder
36

The True Wireless
42

The Home Treatment Of Tuberculosis
By High Frequency Currents
58

WARNING

Remember that the materials and methods described here are from another era. Workers were less safety conscious then, and some methods may be downright dangerous. Be careful! Use good solid judgement in your work, and think ahead. Lindsay Publications Inc. has not tested these methods and materials and does not endorse them. Our job is merely to pass along to you information from another era. Safety is your responsibility.

Write for a complete catalog of unusual books available from:

Lindsay Publications Inc
PO Box 12
Bradley IL 60915-0012

Gravitation and Electricity
by H. Gernsback
Electrical Experimenter, February 1918

In our issue of October, 1916, we mentioned editorially that gravitation was an electromagnetic phenomenon. We also ventured the opinion that what we know as gravitation–like light–probably was only still another manifestation of that mysterious thing we call ether. We furthermore advanced the term of "gravitational waves," to better express our thoughts, because we felt that if gravitation was an electromagnetic phenomenon, it was probably due to a distinct wave motion in the ether.

Up to the time of our writing there did not exist experimental proof that gravitation really was an electromagnetic manifestation of the ether; the ideas in our editorial merely being the rather plausible theories of our leading scientists. To the layman the idea of gravitation being an electric phenomenon came some what as a surprise; nor were there many adherents to the new theory. For, the reasoning was, what electrical force could possibly draw a stone earthward, when released by the hand? But at last experimental proof has been forthcoming through the untiring labors of our brilliant Professor Francis E. Nipher, of the St. Louis Academy of Science. In a pamphlet issued November 8th, 1917, Professor Nipher supplies experimental evidence that gravitational attraction can not only be suspended or nullified by the electrical current, but it actually can be transformed into "gravitational repulsion !"

All during the summer of 1917, Professor Nipher has had his apparatus in almost continuous operation and the experiments have been repeated time and again, always with the same result. To understand better what follows, let us keep in mind the fact that all masses attract each other gravitationally. Thus, for instance, if we suspend a stone by means of a string at sea level, the only mass that will attract the stone will be the earth. In this case the stone will hang absolutely vertical, i.e., at right angles to the earth. But take the same stone with its string and carry it up a mountain, let us say half way up, then the earth, too, will still attract the stone. But so will the large mass of the mountain, with the result that the string will not hang absolutely at right angles to the level of the earth, but the stone will be pulled *slightly towards the mountain,* because of the attracting mass of the mountain.

Professor Nipher's apparatus briefly consists of two large lead spheres ten inches in diameter, resting upon heavy sheets of hard rubber. Two small lead balls, each one inch in diameter were now suspended from two silk threads, stationed at the sides of the two large lead spheres, from which they were separated a little distance. Moreover, the suspended balls were insulated elaborately from the large spheres by enclosing them first airtight in a long wooden box, which was also covered with tinned iron sheets as well as cardboard sheets. There was furthermore a metal shield between the box and the large metal spheres. The large metal lead spheres now exerted a certain gravitational pull upon the suspended small lead balls, just as the mountain attracted our stone as mentioned before. The silk suspension threads therefore did not form a "plumb-line" but the small lead balls were slightly pulled over towards the large spheres.

Now, Professor Nipher applied an electrical current to the large spheres–20 amperes alternating current. The gravitational attraction was quickly reduced to zero, and not only that but in 15 to 20 minutes the small lead spheres *had moved away over one-half as much to the opposite direction* as the distance they had been attracted originally towards the large masses. Thus gravitation had not only been completely nullified, but it was *actually reversed.*

This is equivalent to our stone rushing skyward when released, instead of falling to the earth!

Prof. Nipher's historic experiment is certainly one of the most important discoveries of the century. When it leaves the laboratory, as it surely shall, it will not only revolutionize the world, but it will make man free from his gravitational fetters that now chain him to the earth like a rock.

H. GERNSBACK.

Can Electricity Destroy Gravitation?

Electrical Experimenter, March 1918

Is it possible to nullify, and further, to even reverse, the effect of gravity by electricity ? This scientific conundrum seems about to be solved at least to a certain extent. To begin with, everybody is familiar with that law of physics which states "that all particles of matter attract each other with a force which is greater, the nearer the particles are together," and to be still more definite, Newton's law says that bodies behave as if every particle of matter attracted every other particle with a force that is proportional to the product of their masses and inversely proportional to the square of the distance between them. It is the gravitational attraction between the earth and the bodies upon it which causes the latter to have *weight*.

This fact is often lost sight of and should be well understood by every student. To make the matter more clear let us imagine that a man's body is (as by flying, jumping, diving from a high point, etc.) for the moment separated from the surface of the earth. As soon as the mass of the body is separated from the earth, gravitational attraction is set up between the two masses. The earth pulls the man's body, and also his body pulls the earth, but as the mass of the earth is infinitely greater, its movement cannot be detected.

The scientists of today believe that in some mysterious way the minute electrical charges existing on the particles making up molecules and atoms are definitely linked up and concerned with such basic phenomena as *gravitation*. Since all bodies are made up of atoms it would seem to logically follow that the forces of gravity must depend in some way upon attractions which atoms exert upon

each other, and due to the fact that the atoms are separated, at least in solids and liquids, by extremely small distances, we might expect these inter-atomic forces to be relatively more powerful than are those of ordinary gravitation. Until recently, however, the mystery linking this inter-atomic activity with the force of gravitation baffled all attempts at solution, although many scientists had tackled it.

But at last experimental proof has been forthcoming through the untiring efforts of Professor Francis E. Nipher, of the St. Louis Academy of Science. In a pamphlet issued November 8th 1917, Professor Nipher supplies experimental evidence that gravitational attraction can not only be suspended or nullified by the electrical current, but it actually can

Prof. Francis E. Nipher, of the St. Louis Academy of Science, Who Has Proved By Laboratory Experiments That Gravitation Can Be Nullified and Even Converted Into Repulsion, By Electric Currents Properly Applied.

7

be transformed into gravitational repulsion.

All during the summer of 1917, Professor Nipher had his apparatus in almost continual operation and the experiments have been repeated time and again, always with the same result.

Prof. Nipher's mechanical apparatus resembled that used in the "Cavendish experiment," by which it was first experimentally proved that Newton's law of universal gravitational attraction applied to small bodies in their action upon each other of this bar two small lead spheres of known mass. Two equal large balls of solid lead are placed close to the small suspended spheres in the manner shown. Now, remembering our law of physics stated above–that every body in space attracts every other body proportionally to their respective masses and inversely as the distance between them–then it is evident that when this apparatus is set up, that the small suspended spheres will be slightly attracted by the larger, stationary balls. This condition is represented in Fig. 1.

Before connecting any form of electric current to the modified Cavendish apparatus, Prof. Nipher took special precaution to care-

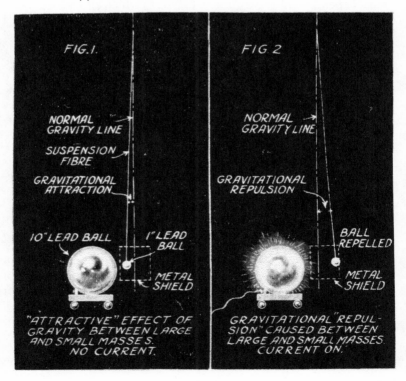

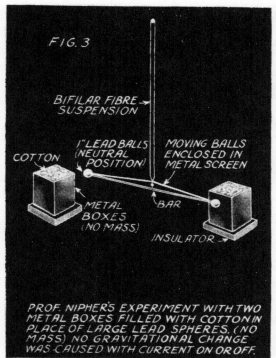

Several Simple Diagrams Which Show, In a Manner Understandable to All, the Essence of the Epoch-making Experiments on the Effect of Electricity on Gravitation, as Conducted by Prof. Nipher at Washington University, St. Louis, Mo.

FIG. 3

BIFILAR FIBRE
SUSPENSION

COTTON

1" LEAD BALLS
(NEUTRAL
POSITION)

MOVING BALLS
ENCLOSED IN
METAL SCREEN

METAL
BOXES
(NO MASS)

BAR

INSULATOR

PROF. NIPHER'S EXPERIMENT WITH TWO METAL BOXES FILLED WITH COTTON IN PLACE OF LARGE LEAD SPHERES. (NO MASS) NO GRAVITATIONAL CHANGE WAS CAUSED WITH CURRENT ON OR OFF.

fully screen the moving element from any electro-static or electro-magnetic effects. His apparatus briefly consists of two large lead spheres ten inches in diameter, resting upon heavy sheets of hard rubber. Two small lead balls, each one inch in diameter were now suspended from two silk threads, stationed at the sides of the two large lead spheres, from which they were separated a little distance. Moreover, the suspended balls were insulated elaborately from the large spheres by enclosing them first airtight in a long wooden box, which was also covered with tinned iron sheets as well as cardboard sheets. There was, furthermore, a metal shield between the box and the large metal spheres. The large metal lead spheres now exerted a certain gravitational pull upon the suspended small lead balls as indicated in Fig. 1, and the small lead balls were slightly pulled over towards the large spheres.

In his first experiments Prof. Nipher applied a high tension current from a static machine to the large lead balls, see Fig. 2. No difference was noted whether the positive or negative terminals were applied. In one of these experiments the masses were "repelled"

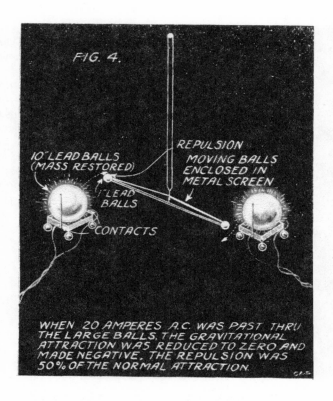

FIG. 4.

10" LEAD BALLS
(MASS RESTORED)

1" LEAD
BALLS

CONTACTS

REPULSION
MOVING BALLS
ENCLOSED IN
METAL SCREEN

WHEN 20 AMPERES A.C. WAS PAST THRU
THE LARGE BALLS, THE GRAVITATIONAL
ATTRACTION WAS REDUCED TO ZERO AND
MADE NEGATIVE, THE REPULSION WAS
50% OF THE NORMAL ATTRACTION.

(normal gravitational *attraction* had been nullified and changed to *repulsion*) by a force nearly twice as great as the initial gravitational repulsion. This effect is shown at Fig. 2.

In further experiments Prof. Nipher decided to check his results. To do this he replaced the large solid lead spheres with two metal boxes, each filled with loose cotton batting. These hollow boxes (having practically no mass) rested upon insulators. They were separated from the protective screen by sheets of glass and were *grounded* to it by heavy copper wires. The metal boxes were then charged in every way that the solid lead spheres had been, but *not the slightest change in the position of the suspended balls could be detected.* This would seem to prove conclusively that the "repulsion" and "gravitational nullification" effects that he had produced when the solid large balls were electrically charged, were genuine and based undoubtedly on a true *inter-atomic electrical reaction,* and not upon any form of electro-static or electro-magnetic effects between the large and small masses. If they had been, the metal boxes, with no

10

mass, would have served as well as the solid balls.

Another interesting experiment was conducted with low frequency alternating current applied to the large lead spheres. Spring contact brushes were fastened to the wooden blocks supporting the large spheres as shown in Fig. 4, one brush on either side of the ball. This permitted sending current through the ball from one side to the other. First, a direct current of 20 amperes was sent through the two large masses, but no effect upon the suspended masses could be detected. Next, an alternating current of 20 amperes was sent through the large masses, see Fig. 4, with the result that the gravitational attraction was quickly reduced to zero, and not only that but in 15 to 20 minutes the small lead spheres *had moved away over one-half as much to the opposite direction* as the distance they had been attracted originally towards the large masses. Thus gravitation had not only been completely nullified, but it was *actually reversed.*

A Novel Tesla Steam Electric Clock

Electrical Experimenter, April 1917

Among the various wonderful inventions of Dr. Nikola Tesla we find one of the most interesting clocks ever made, and the accompanying photographs show the necessary equipment for this highly ingenious and novel electric clock.

The clock proper, shown above, is apparently no different from any other standard clock. However, the mechanical movement has been removed and substituted by another special movement linked up with an alternating current motor of special construction which can be seen at the extreme right of the clock. The field consists of a number of rectangular coils placed in toroidal form and connected in series. The rotor or armature is constructed of a circular iron disc, the periphery of which consists of a large number of poles. The speed of this rotor is controlled by the current input. Connections between the rotor shaft and that of the clock hands is obtained by means of a number of reduction gears properly calculated so as to obtain the correct time, when the hands are acted upon by the motor.

The source of current for driving this remarkable electric clock motor is obtained from an alternating current generator of very unique construction and design, this machine being illustrated here. It consists of two steam or compressed air cylinders, built in one frame as shown. A piston is placed in each of the cylinders which operate

A Steam-Electric Clock Devised Some Years Ago by Dr. Nikola Tesla, the Electrical Wizard. It Comprises an Air or Steam Engine Which Operates Two Special Oscillating Alternators. These Are Wired Up to a Special Motor on the Clock—the Entire Combination Keeping Extremely Accurate Time, It Is Said.

alternately with respect to each other. The connecting rods of each piston are linked with a vibrating membrane of each dynamo; these are seen at each end. A coil is placed on each membrane and connected to a special commutator. The electro-magnet or coil is operated in a powerful magnetic field, made up of two powerful electro-magnets placed at each end of the generator. These coils are excited by a direct current, while the coil on the vibrating disk is utilized to supply the alternating current.

The operation of this type of machine may be explained as follows: When the steam or compressed air is permitted to enter the cylinders, thus operating the pistons and in turn vibrating the armatures or coils, an electro-motive force is induced in the coil by virtue of being moved in the magnetic field surrounding it. The period or frequency of vibration of this current depends upon the rapidity of the armature movement. Both generators are linked in such a manner that an alternating current of uniform form and periodicity is obtained.

The motor on the clock is connected with this special generator and the current is so adjusted that a uniform velocity of the rotor is always obtained in order to obtain absolutely correct time from the clock.

A large number of such clocks were installed in the laboratory of Dr. Nikola Tesla a number of years ago which are driven by a single generating unit. It is said that the accuracy of time attained by this ingenious clock system is far better than with any other system known.

The Electrical Production of Synthetic Gasoline

Electrical Experimenter, April 1918

The world needs gasoline–thousands of internal combustion engines are daily consuming untold gallons of the valuable fuel and have sent the price skyward at a rate that would give the average motorist heart failure. And just at the time that the situation promised to become acute, an inventor comes forward with an electrical method of producing it from kerosene, solar oil and low grade distillates.

Briefly the process is as follows: Take some kerosene, vaporize it, mix in a little natural gas and shoot a bolt of electricity thru it. Wash with acid, soda ash and water, then distill and you

Mr. Louis Bond Cherry, Inventor of the Electrical Process for Making Gaso-

have pure, water white gasoline that will clean kid gloves or drive a motor car. Simple, isn't it?

But it took two years of experimental work to bring the process to its present practical condition. One of the illustrations show Mr.

General View of High Tension Gallery Containing Step-Up Transformers Used in the New Cherry Process of Producing Gasoline

Louis B. Cherry, the inventor of the process, and the first plant that proved his ideas practical.

In order to understand the working of the Cherry process for producing gasoline it would not be out of place to describe briefly the usual process of distillation of crude oil. Then a better idea will be gained of how the new process can be readily adopted to the present refineries.

The oil as it comes from the well is black in color, having a disagreeable odor and quite thick. In this form it is known as crude oil and, depending on the part of the country from which it comes, will have very little gasoline, or possibly as high as 15 to 30 per cent of gasoline, in it.

This oil is pumped into a large still which may hold from five to fifteen hundred barrels. This still is usually of cylindrical form and is mounted on brickwork similar to a horizontal steam boiler. Fire is placed under the still and the temperature of the oil gradually raised. When it reaches a temperature of 90 to 100 degrees, Fahrenheit, gases will pass over into a condenser which consists of a large coiled pipe immersed in a tank of water. These vapors condense and thus is obtained high proof gasoline or petroleum ether.

The temperature is further raised until all the gasoline vapor passes over. The end point or the maximum temperature at which gases are allowed to pass over is 400 deg. F. This fraction or *cut* is known as crude benzine by the refiners and is then treated with sulfuric acid, soda ash, washed with water and redistilled. This results in the commercial gasoline used for motor cars.

The above process takes out all the gasoline, further heating causes kerosene, solar oil and heavy lubricating oils to pass

Switch-board equipment for Controlling the High Frequency Oscillating Current Used in Making Gasoline for 10 Cents a Gallon.

Upper End of Pipe Treatment Chambers, Show 100,000 Volt Insulators

First Demonstration Plant for Producing Gasoline by Electricity

over and condense in turn. This operation is known as *fractional distillation,* the residue remaining in the still after a high temperature is reached being coal tar, which is the source of our dyes and other products.

Now turning to the Cherry process. It is a well-known fact that all crude oil products from gasoline to paraffin wax are hydrocarbons–that is, they consist of varying mixtures of hydrogen and carbon. It is apparent that were some means found for controlling the relative proportions of the hydrogen and carbon it would be possible to produce any of the various products at will; that is, obtain all paraffin or all gasoline, as desired. By studying the constituents of the various hydrocarbons, Mr. Cherry noted the fact that if natural gas could be combined chemically in proper proportions with the various distillates, he would then have gasoline. Acting on this he discovered that a high-tension electric current would affect the necessary reaction and produce gasoline.

In practice, the still used is similar to that employed in refining crude oil, but has a perforated pipe at the bottom. The kerosene or other low-grade oil is placed in this still and while being heated natural gas is forced into the perforated pipe and escaping up thru the liquid is heated to the same temperature and thoroughly mixed with the oil vapor. This vapor then passes into a series of electrically heated pipes that have a central electrode, this electrode as well as the pipes being connected to a source of high-tension current of extremely high frequency.

The gases are subjected to this silent discharge as they flow thru the pipes and their chemical structure is so altered that the resulting condensate is a crude benzine. For the proper results it is necessary

15

that the temperature of the gases, their rate of flow, as well as the voltage and frequency of the current be properly adjusted. On treating the benzine so obtained a liquid results that cannot be detected from gasoline in fact, it is gasoline!

To produce 60,000 gallons of gasoline by the above process daily. an electrical equipment rated at 75 K.W. (75,000 watts) is required. The illustrations give a good idea of the apparatus employed in a plant of the above size. The general view of the high-tension gallery shows the transformer in the background, with the condenser used in the closed oscillating circuit at the left. Another illustration shows the rotary spark gap having two large rotating disks fitted with plugs to obtain a high rate of discharge thru the closed circuit, the primary of the oscillatory transformer being shown at the left.

The treating chambers are shown in another illustration in which the mixed vapors are treated. The large porcelain insulators can be clearly seen that insulate the central electrodes. The pipes are also wound with electric heating coils to obtain the proper temperature.

All this apparatus is controlled from a switch-board that is shown in another illustration, which also mounts the meters that indicate the currents flowing in the different circuits at any time.

The entire operation taking place at atmospheric pressure, it is a simple matter to fit the ordinary crude oil still with the necessary treating chambers and electrical equipment. Tests tend to prove that the cost of treating *one gallon of kerosene does not exceed one cent,* while the value of the process will be better appreciated when it is stated that it is practical to convert nearly all the volatile oils into gasoline without undue precipitation of carbon or the production of fixt gases.

Oscillatory Spark Gap, for Interrupting 75 K.W. at 100,000 Volts

At a recent test *it was possible to change 78.68 per cent of the kerosene used into pure gasoline, but the plant under construction is expected to raise the percentage to 98 or 100.* Mr. Cherry has offered to furnish the government all the gasoline it requires for a flat rate of 10 *cents per gallon,* and to say the least this offer has caused quite a commotion among those interested in gasoline production.

Is this but another step along the road to the production of gold from the baser metals? According to the more recent theories of the electrical nature of matter it should be possible to affect such a change by electrical means. All matter being made up of electrical charges, it merely remains for some one to find a way of controlling the grouping of these charges and they can instantly produce anything from the material in hand.

The kerosene vapor with which has been mixed natural gas, enters at A and passes into pipe B. The latter is of iron covered with a layer of electrical insulation, such as mica, shown at F, over which is wound the resistance wires G, for heating the chamber. These wires are in turn covered by a thick layer of heat insulating material to retain the heat and keep the temperature constant.

The electrode D is mounted centrally in the chamber, being supported and insulated by the porcelain E. At J is shown the terminals of the heating winding.

The sectional view also shows the wiring to produce the high tension high frequency currents required to treat the vapors. An alternating current supply is connected to the primary of the step-up transformer T, thru a choke coil CC. A condenser C is shunted across the secondary of the transformer, while a rotary spark gap R serves to discharge the condenser periodically through the primary of the oscillation transformer O.T. In this manner high frequency currents are induced in the secondary of the oscillation transformer which flow to the rods D, connection being made from the other terminal to the pipes as shown at I.

The heating coils are connected to the current supply through an adjustable resistance not shown in the drawing.

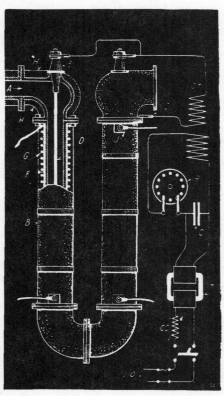

Sectional View of Electrified High-Tension Vapor Chambers Used in Producing Synthetic Gasoline.

Tesla's Egg of Columbus

How Tesla Performed the Feat
without Cracking the Egg

Electrical Experimenter, March 1919

Probably one of the most far reaching and revolutionary discoveries made by Mr. Tesla is the so-called *rotating magnetic field*. This is a new and wonderful manifestation of force–a magnetic cyclone–producing striking phenomena which amazed the world when first shown by him. It results from the joint action of two or more alternating currents definitely related to one another and creating magnetic fluxes, which, by their periodic rise and fall according to a mathematical law, cause a continuous shifting of the lines of force. There is a vast difference between an ordinary electromagnet and that invented by Tesla. In the former the lines are stationary, in the latter they are made to whirl around at a furious rate. The first attracts a piece of iron and holds it fast; the second causes it to spin in any direction and with any speed desired. Long ago, when Tesla was still a student, he conceived the idea of the rotating magnetic field and this remarkable principle is embodied in his famous *induction motor* and system of transmission of power now in universal use.

In this issue of the Electrical Experimenter inventor Mr. Tesla gives a remarkable account of his early efforts and trials as an inventor and of his final success. Unlike other technical advances arrived at through the usual hit and miss methods and haphazard experimentation, the rotating field was purely the work of scientific imagination. Tesla developed and perfected, entirely in his mind, this great idea in all its details and applications *without making one single experiment*. Not even the usual first model was used. When the various forms of apparatus he had devised were tried for the first time they worked exactly as he had imagined and he took out some forty fundamental patents covering the whole vast region he had explored. He obtained the first rotations in the summer of 1883 after five years of constant and intense thought on the subject and then undertook the equally difficult task of finding believers in his discovery. The alternating current was but imperfectly understood and had no standing with engineers or electricians and for a long time Tesla talked to deaf ears. But, ultimately, his pains were rewarded and early in 1887

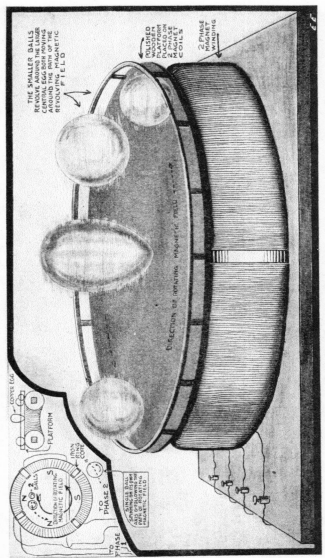

Fig. 2. Illustrating the Polyphase Coil and Rotating Magnetic Field Which Caused Copper Eggs to Spin.
Fig. 3. Insert: Detail of Coil Apparatus Showing Coil Connections to Different Phases.

a company bearing his name was formed for the commercial introduction of the invention.

Dr. Tesla recently told the editors an amusing incident in this connection. He had approached a Wall Street capitalist–a prominent lawyer–with a view of getting financial support and this gentle-

Fig. 1. This hitherto unpublished photograph is extremely interesting as it shows not only Tesla's Electric Egg apparatus in the center of the background, but also a comprehensive view of a corner of his famous Houston Street laboratory of a decade ago. At the left may be seen a number of Tesla's oscillators or high frequency generator, while in the rear may be noted a large high frequency transformer of the spiral type, the diameter of which was at little over nine feet. The electric egg apparatus comprising a two-phase A.C. circular core and winding, rests on a table, and this particular model measured about two feet across. In making the demonstrations. Tesla applied as much as 200 H.P. from a two-phase alternator to the exciting coils, and so intense was the revolving magnetic field created in the surrounding space, that small delicately pivoted iron discs would revolve in any part of the hall, and a great many other devices

could be simultaneously operated from this magnetic field when thus excited. The frequency of the two - phase A.C. energizing the coils, was varied from 25 to 300 cycles, the best results being obtained with currents of from 35 to 40 cycles; This laboratory was lighted by Tesla's vacuum tubes, several of: which may be seen on the ceiling and each of which emitted 50 C.P. The coil resting on three legs and observed in the immediate foreground is the primary of a resonant Tesla transformer which collected energy from an oscillatory circuit encircling the laboratory, no matter in what position the transformer was placed. A low tension secondary of one or two turns of heavy cable (not visible) was provided for stepping down the energy collected by "mutual induction" and supplied the current to incandescent lamps, vacuum tubes, motors and other devices. When the circuit around the hall was strongly excited, the secondary furnished energy at the rate of about three - quarters of one horse-power.

man called in a friend of his, a well-known engineer at the head of one of the big corporations in New York, to pass upon the merits of the scheme. This man was a practical expert who knew of the failures in the industrial exploitation of alternating currents and was distinctly prejudiced to a point of not caring even to witness some tests. After several discouraging conferences Mr. Tesla had an inspiration. Everybody has heard of the "Egg of Columbus." The saying goes that at a certain dinner the great explorer asked some scoffers of his project to balance an egg on its end. They tried it in vain. He then took it and cracking the shell slightly by a gentle blow, made it stand upright. This may be a myth but the fact is that he was granted an audience by Isabella, the Queen of Spain, and won her support. There is a suspicion that she was more imprest by his portly bearing than the prospect of his discovery. Whatever it might have been, the Queen pawned her jewels and three ships were equipped for him and so it happened that the Germans got all that was coming to them in this war. But to return to Tesla's reminiscence. He said to these men, "Do you know the story of the Egg of Columbus?" Of course they did. "Well," he continued, "what if I could make an egg stand on the pointed end without cracking the shell ?" "If you could do this we would admit that you had gone Columbus one better." "And would you be willing to go out of your way as much as Isabella?" "We have no crown jewels to pawn," said the lawyer, who was a wit, "but there are a few ducats in our buckskins and we might help you to an extent."

Mr. Tesla thus succeeded in capturing the attention and personal interest of these very busy men, extremely conservative and reluctant to go into any new enterprise, and the rest was easy. He arranged for a demonstration the following day. A rotating field magnet was fastened under the top board of a wooden table and Mr.

Tesla provided a copper plated egg and several brass balls and pivoted iron discs for convincing his prospective associates. He placed the egg on the table and, to their astonishment, it stood on end, but when they found that it was *rapidly spinning* their stupefaction was complete. The brass balls and pivoted iron discs in turn were set spinning rapidly by the rotating field, to the amazement of the spectators. No sooner had they regained their composure than Tesla was delighted with the question: "Do you want any money?" "Columbus was never in a worse predicament," said the great inventor, who had parted with his last portrait of George Washington in defraying the expenses of the preparation. Before the meeting adjourned he had a substantial check in his pocket, and it was given with the assurance that there was more to be had in the same bank. That started the ball rolling. Tens of millions of horsepower of Tesla's induction motors are now in use all over the world and their production is rising like a flood.

In 1893 Mr. Albert Schmid, then Superintendent of the Westinghouse Electric and Mfg. Co. constructed a powerful rotating field ring with an egg made of copper, and larger than that of an ostrich, for Dr. Tesla's personal collection at the Chicago World's Fair. This piece of apparatus was one of the most attractive novelties ever publicly shown and drew enormous crowds every day. Subsequently it was taken to Mr. Tesla's laboratory and served there permanently for demonstrating rotating field phenomena. In his experiments it was practicable to use as much as 200 *horsepower* for a short time, without overheating the wires and the effects of the magnetic forces were wonderfully fascinating to observe. This is the very ring indicated in the accompanying photograph (Fig. 1), giving a view of Mr. Tesla's former laboratory at 46 E. Houston Street, New York. It is shown in detail in Fig. 2, and the mode of winding is illustrated. in diagram (Fig. 3). Originally the two-phase arrangement was provided but Mr. Tesla transformed it to the three and four phase when desired. On top of the ring was fastened a thin circular board, slightly hollowed, and provided around its circumference with a guard to prevent the objects from flying off.

Even more interesting than the spinning egg was the exhibition of *planetary motion*. In this experiment one large, and several small brass balls were usually employed. When the field was energized all the balls would be set spinning, the large one remaining in the center while the small ones revolved around it, like moons about a planet, gradually receding until they reached the outer guard and raced along the same.

But the demonstration which most impressed the audiences was the simultaneous operation of numerous balls, pivoted discs and other

Fig. 5. This Illustration shows one of Tesla's high frequency oscillation generators and a bank of his high frequency lamps lighted by the same. These highly evacuated, gas filled tubes were operated in different ways. In some cases they were connected to one wire only; in other instances to two wires, in the manner of ordinary incandescent lamps. Often, however, they were operated without any connection to wires at all. i.e., by "wireless energy," over quite appreciable distances, which could have been greatly extended with more power. The oscillator comprises a Tesla high potential transformer which is excited from a condenser and circuit controllers as described in his patents of 1896. The primary exciting element comprised a powerful electro-magnet actuating an armature, and this circuit was connected with 110 volt 60 cycle A.C. or D.C. When the oscillator was put Into operation, the interrupter actuated by the electro-magnet connected to the 110 volt circuit, became simultaneously the spark gap for the high potential exciting circuit which included this vibrator spark gap, a high tension condenser and the primary of the high frequency Tesla transformer. The lamps were connected to the secondary of the latter–the terminals of which are seen In the rear of the machine.

devices placed in all sorts of positions and *at considerable distances from the rotating field.* When the currents were turned on and the whole animated with motion, it presented an unforgettable spectacle. Mr. Tesla had many vacuum bulbs in which small, light metal discs were pivotally arranged on jewels and these would spin anywhere in the hall when the iron ring was energized.

Rotating fields of 15,000 horsepower are now being turned out by the leading manufacturers and it is very likely that in the near future capacities of 50,000 horsepower will be employed in the steel

Fig. 4. This photograph represents a collection of a few of Tesla's wireless lamps, such as he proposes to use in lighting isolated dwellings all over the world from central wireless plants. The two lamps at either corner at the bottom are illuminated, owing to the fact that a high frequency oscillator was in operation some distance away when this photograph was being taken. These tubes were filled with various gases for experimental research work in determining which was most efficient.

and other industries and ship propulsion by Tesla's electric drive which, according to Secretary of the Navy Daniels' statement, has proved a great success.

But any student interested in these phenomena can repeat all the classical experiments of Tesla by inexpensive apparatus. For this purpose it is only necessary to make two slip ring connections on an ordinary small direct current motor or dynamo and to wind an iron ring with four coils as indicated in diagram Fig. 3. No particular rule need be given for the windings but it may be stated that he will get the best results if he will use an iron ring of comparatively *small section* and wind it *with as many turns of stout wire as practicable.* He can heavily copper plate an egg but he should bear in mind that Tesla's egg is not as innocent as that of Columbus. The worst that can happen with the latter is that it might be,–er,–overripe! but the Tesla egg may explode with disastrous effect because the copper plating is apt to be brought to a high temperature thru the induced currents. The sensible experimenter will, therefore, first suck out the contents of the egg thus satisfying both his appetite and thirst for knowledge.

Besides the rotating field apparatus Mr. Tesla had other surprises for his audiences, which were even more wonderful. So, for instance, the coil on three legs, visible in the foreground, was used to operate wireless motors, lamps and other devices, and the spiral coil in the background served to show extraordinary high potential phenomena, as streamers of great length.

My Inventions; The Discovery of the Tesla Coil and Transformer

by N. Tesla

Electrical Experimenter, May 1919

For a while I gave myself up entirely to the intense enjoyment of picturing machines and devising new forms. It was a mental state of happiness about as complete as I have ever known in life. Ideas came in an uninterrupted stream and the only difficulty I had was to hold them fast. The pieces of apparatus I conceived were to me absolutely real and tangible in every detail, even to the minutest marks and signs of wear. I delighted in imagining the motors constantly running, for in this way they presented to the mind's eye a more fascinating sight. When natural inclination develops into a passionate desire, one advances towards his goal in seven-league boots. In less than two months I evolved virtually all the types of motors and modifications of the system which are now identified with my name. It was, perhaps, providential that the necessities of existence commanded a temporary halt to this consuming activity of the mind. I came to Budapest prompted by a premature report concerning the telephone enterprise and, as irony or fate willed it, I had to accept a position as draftsman in the Central Telegraph Office of the Hungarian Government at a salary which I deem it my privilege not to disclose! Fortunately, I soon won the interest of the Inspector-in-Chief and was thereafter employed on calculations, designs and estimates in connection with new installations, until the Telephone Exchange was started, when I took charge of the same. The knowledge and practical experience I gained in the course of this work was most valuable and the employment gave me ample opportunities for the exercise of my inventive faculties. I made several improvements in the Central Station apparatus and perfected a telephone repeater or amplifier which was never patented or publicly described but would be creditable to me even today. In recognition of my efficient assis-

Fig. 1—Tesla Oscillation Transformer (Tesla Coil) Presented by Lord Kelvin Before the British Association in August, 1897. This Small and Compact Instrument, Only 8 Inches High, Developed Two Square Feet of Streamers With Twenty Five Watts From the 110 Volt D.C. Supply Circuit. The Instrument Contains a Tesla Primary and Secondary, Condenser, and a Circuit Controller.

tance the organizer of the undertaking, Mr. Puskas, upon disposing of his business in Budapest, offered me a position in Paris which I gladly accepted.

I never can forget the deep impression that magic city produced on my mind. For several days after my arrival I roamed thru the streets in utter bewilderment of the new spectacle. The attractions were many and irresistible, but, alas, the income was spent as soon as received. When Mr. Puskas asked me how I was getting along in the new sphere, I described the situation accurately in the statement that "the last twenty-nine days of the month are the toughest !" I led a rather strenuous life in what would now be termed "Rooseveltian fashion." Every morning, regardless of weather, I would go from the Boulevard St. Marcel, where I resided, to a bathing house on the Seine, plunge into the water, loop the circuit twenty-seven times and then walk an hour to reach Ivry, where the Company's factory was located. There I would have a woodchopper's breakfast at half-past seven o'clock and then eagerly await the lunch hour, in the meanwhile cracking hard nuts for the Manager of the Works, Mr. Charles Batchellor, who was an intimate friend and assistant of Edison. Here I was thrown in contact with a few Americans who fairly fell in love with me because of my proficiency in billiards. To these men I explained my invention and one of them, Mr. D. Cunningham, Foreman of the Mechanical Department, offered to form a stock company. The proposal seemed to me comical in the extreme. I did not have the faintest conception of what that meant except that it was an American way of doing things. Nothing came of it, however, and during the next few months I had to travel from one to another place in France and Germany to cure the ills of the power plants. On my return to Paris I submitted to one of the administrators of the Company, Mr. Rau, a plan for improving their dynamos and was given an opportunity. My success was complete and the delighted directors accorded me the privilege of developing automatic regulators which were much desired. Shortly after there was some trouble with the lighting plant which has been installed at the new railroad station in Strasburg, Alsace. The wiring was defective and on the occasion of the opening ceremonies a large part of a wall was blown out through a short-circuit right in the presence of old Emperor William I. The German Government refused to take the plant and the French Company was facing a serious loss. On account of my knowledge of the German language and past experience, I was entrusted with the difficult task of straightening out matters and early in 1883 I went to Strasburg on that mission.

Fig. 2—This Illustrates Tests With Spark Discharges From a Ball of Forty Centimeters Radius in Tesla's Wireless Plant Erected at Colorado Springs in 1899. The Ball Is Connected to the Free End of a Grounded Resonant Circuit Seventeen Meters in Diameter. The Disruptive Potential of a Ball, is, According to Tesla, in Volts Approximately V = 75,400 r (r Being in Centimeters), That Is, in This Case 75,400 x 40 – 3,016,000 Volts. The Gigantic Tesla Coil Which Produced These Bolts of Thor Was Capable of Furnishing a Current of 1,100 Amperes In the High Tension Secondary. The Primary Coil Had a Diameter of 51 Feet! This Tesla Coil Produced Discharges Which Were the Nearest Approach to Lightning Ever Made by Man.

The First Induction Motor Is Built.
Some of the incidents in that city have left an indelible record on my memory. By a curious coincidence, a number of men who subsequently achieved fame, lived there about that time. In later life I used to say, "There were bacteria of greatness in that old town. Others caught the disease but I escaped!" The practical work, correspondence, and conferences with officials kept me preoccupied day and night, but as soon as I was able to manage I undertook the construction of a simple motor in a mechanical shop opposite the railroad station, having brought with me from Paris some material for that purpose. The consummation of the experiment was, however, delayed until the summer of that year when I finally had the satisfaction of *seeing rotation effected by alternating currents of different phase, and without sliding contacts or commutator,* as I had conceived a year before. It was an exquisite pleasure but not to compare with the delirium of joy following the first revelation.

Among my new friends was the former Mayor of the city, Mr. Bauzin, whom I had already in a measure acquainted with this and other inventions of mine and whose support I endeavored to enlist. He was sincerely devoted to me and put my project before several wealthy persons but, to my mortification, found no response. He wanted to help me in every possible way and the approach of the first of July, 1919, happens to remind me of a form of "assistance" I received from that charming man, which was not financial but none the less appreciated. In 1870, when the Germans invaded the country, Mr. Bauzin had buried a good sized allotment of St. Estephe of 1801 and he came to the conclusion that he knew no worthier person than myself to consume that precious beverage. This, I may say, is one of the unforgettable incidents to which I have referred. My friend urged me to return to Paris as soon as possible and seek support there. This I was anxious to do but my work and negotiations were protracted owing to all sorts of petty obstacles I encountered so that at times the situation seemed hopeless.

German "Efficiency"
Just to give an idea of German thoroughness and "efficiency," I may mention here a rather funny experience. An incandescent lamp of 16 c.p. was to be placed in a hallway and upon selecting the proper location I ordered the *monteur* to run the wires. After working for a while he concluded that the engineer had to be consulted and this was done. The latter made several objections but ultimately agreed that the lamp should be placed two inches from the spot I had assigned, whereupon the work proceeded. Then the engineer became worried and told me that Inspector Averdeck should be no-

tified. That important person called, investigated, debated, and decided that the lamp should be shifted back two inches, which was the place I had marked. It was not long, however, before Averdeck got cold feet himself and advised me that he had informed *Ober-Inspector* Hieronimus of the matter and that I should await his decision. It was several days before the *Ober-Inspector* was able to free himself of other pressing duties but at last he arrived and a two hour debate followed, when he decided to move the lamp two inches farther. My hopes that this was the final act were shattered when the *Ober-Inspector* returned and said to me: "*Regierungsrath Funke* is so particular that I would not dare to give an order for placing this lamp without his explicit approval." Accordingly arrangements for a visit from that great man were made. We started cleaning up and polishing early in the morning Funke came with his retinue he was ceremoniously received. After two hours' deliberation he suddenly exclaimed: "I must be going," and pointing to a place on the ceiling, he ordered me to put the morning.[sic] Everybody brushed up, I put on my gloves and when lamp there.[sic] It was the exact spot which I had originally chosen.

So it went day after day with variations, but I was determined to achieve at whatever cost and in the end my efforts were rewarded. By the spring of 1884 all the differences were adjusted, the plant formally accepted, and I returned to Paris with pleasing anticipations. One of the administrators had promised me a liberal compensation in case I succeeded, as well as a fair consideration of the improvements I had made in their dynamos and I hoped to realize a substantial sum. There were three administrators whom I shall designate as A, B and C for convenience. When I called on A. *he* told me that B had the say. This gentleman thought that only C could decide and the latter was quite sure that A alone had the power to act. After several laps of this *circulus viscous* it dawned upon me that my reward was a castle in Spain. The utter failure of my attempts to raise capital for development was another disappointment and when Mr. Batchellor pressed me to go to America with a view of redesigning the Edison machines, I determined to try my fortunes in the Land of Golden Promise. But the chance was nearly mist. I liquefied my modest assets, secured accommodations and found myself at the railroad station as the train was pulling out. At that moment I discovered that my money and tickets were gone. What to do was the question. Hercules had plenty of time to deliberate but I had to decide while running alongside the train with opposite feelings surging in my brain like condenser oscillations. Resolve, helped by dexterity, won out in the nick of time and upon passing thru the usual experiences, as trivial as unpleasant, I managed to embark for New

York with the remnants of my belongings, some poems and articles I had written, and a package of calculations relating to solutions of an unsolvable integral and to my flying machine. During the voyage I sat most of the time at the stern of the ship watching for an opportunity to save somebody from a watery grave, without the slightest

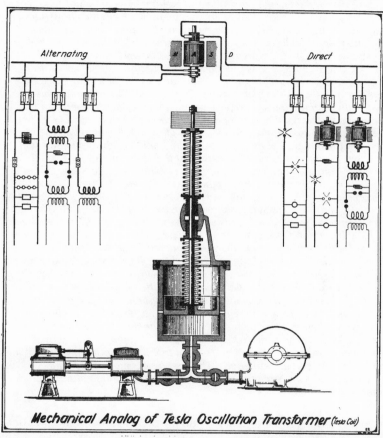

Mechanical Analog of Tesla Oscillation Transformer (Tesla Coil)

This revolutionary improvement was exhibited and explained by Tesla for the first time in his lecture before the American Institute of Electrical Engineers May 20, 1891. It has made possible to generate automatically damped or undamped oscillations of any desired frequency and, what is equally important, of perfectly constant period. It has been instrumental in many great achievements and its use has become universal. The underlying principle may be briefly stated as follows: A source of electricity is made to charge a condenser and when the difference of potential at the terminals of the latter has reached a predetermined value an air-gap is

31

bridged, permitting the accumulated energy to be discharged through a circuit under resonant conditions, this resulting in a long series of isochronous impulses. These are either directly used or converted to any desired volume or pressure by means of a second circuit inductively linked with the first and tuned to the same. The above diagram is taken from Tesla's lecture before the Franklin Institute and National Electric Light Association in 1893 and shows more elaborate arrangements of circuits, now quite familiar, for the conversion of ordinary direct or alternating currents into high frequency oscillations by this general method. In the mechanical apparatus illustrated, an attempt is made to convey an idea of the electrical operations as closely as practicable. The reciprocating and centrifugal pumps, respectively, represent an alternating and a direct current generator. The water takes the place of the electric fluid. The cylinder with its elastically restrained piston represents the condenser. The inertia of the moving parts corresponds to the self-induction of the electric circuit and the wide ports around the cylinder, through which the fluid can escape, perform the function of the air-gap. The operation of this apparatus will now be readily understood. Suppose first that the water is admitted to the cylinder from the centrifugal pump, this corresponding to the action of a continuous current generator. As the fluid is forced into the cylinder, the piston moves upward until the parts are uncovered, when a great quantity of the fluid rushes out, suddenly reducing the pressure so that the force of the compressed spring asserts itself and sends the piston down, closing the ports, whereupon these operations are repeated in as rapid succession as it may be desired. Each time the system, comprising the piston, rod, weights and adjustable spring receives a blow, it quivers at its own rate which is determined by the inertia of the moving parts and the pliability of the spring exactly as in the electrical system the period of the system by the self-induction and capacity. Under the best conditions the natural period of the elastic system will be the same as that of the primarily impressed oscillations, and then the energy of the movement will be greatest. If, instead of the centrifugal, the reciprocating pump is employed, the operation is the same in principle except that the periodic impulses of the pump impose certain limitations. The best results are again obtained when synchronism is maintained between these and the natural oscillations of the system.

thought of danger. Later when I had absorbed some of the practical American sense I shivered at the recollection and marvelled at my former folly.

Tesla in America

I wish that I could put in words my first impressions of this country In the Arabian Tales I read how genii transported people into a land of dreams to live thru delightful adventures. My case was just the reverse. The genii had carried me from a world of dreams into one of realities. What I had left was beautiful, artistic and fascinating in every way; what I saw here was machined, rough and unattractive. A burly policeman was twirling his stick which looked to me as big as a log. I approached him politely with the request to direct me. "Six blocks down, then to the left," he said, with murder in his eyes. "Is this America?" I asked myself in painful surprise. "It is a century behind Europe in civilization." When I went abroad in 1889 five years having elapsed since my arrival here I became convinced that *it was more than one hundred years AHEAD of Europe* and nothing has happened to this day to change my opinion.

Tesla Meets Edison

The meeting with Edison was a memorable event in my life. I was amazed at this wonderful man who, without early advantages and scientific training, had accomplished so much. I had studied a dozen languages, delved in literature and art, and had spent my best years in libraries reading all sorts of stuff that fell into my hands, from Newton's *"Principia"* to the novels of Paul de Kock, and felt that most of my life had been squandered. But it did not take long before I recognized that it was the best thing I could have done. Within a few weeks I had won Edison's confidence and it came about in this way.

The S.S. *Oregon,* the fastest passenger steamer at that time, had both of its lighting machines disabled and its sailing was delayed. As the superstructure had been built after their installation it was impossible to remove them from the hold. The predicament was a serious one and Edison was much annoyed. In the evening I took the necessary instruments with me and went aboard the vessel where I stayed for the night. The dynamos were in bad condition, having several short-circuits and breaks, but with the assistance of the crew I succeeded in putting them in good shape. At five o'clock in the morning, when passing along Fifth Avenue on my way to the shop, I met Edison with Batchellor and a few others as they were returning home to retire. "Here is our Parisian running around at night," he said. When I told him that I was coming from the *Oregon* and had repaired both machines, he looked at me in silence and walked away without another word. But when he had gone some distance I heard him remark: "Batchellor, this is a d–n good man," and from that time on I had full freedom in directing the work. For nearly a year my regular hours were from 10:30 A.M. until 5 o'clock the next morning without a day's exception. Edison said to me: "I have had many hard-working assistants but you take the cake." During this period I designed twenty-four different types of standard machines with short cores and of uniform pattern which replaced the old ones. The Manager had promised me fifty thousand dollars on the completion of this task but it turned out to be a practical joke. This gave me a painful shock and I resigned my position. Immediately thereafter some people approached me with the proposal of forming an arc light company under my name, to which I agreed. Here finally was an opportunity to develop the motor, but when I broached the subject to my new associates they said: "No, we want the arc lamp. We don't care for this alternating current of yours." In 1886 my system of arc lighting was perfected and adopted for factory and municipal lighting, and I was free, but with no other possession than a beautifully engraved certificate of stock of hypothetical value. Then followed a period of struggle in the new medium for which I was not fitted, but the reward came in April, 1887, the Tesla Electric Company was organized, providing a laboratory and facilities. The motors I built there were exactly as I had imagined them. I made no attempt to improve the design, but merely reproduced the pictures as they appeared to my vision and the operation was always as I expected.

In the early part of 1888 an arrangement was made with the Westinghouse Company for the manufacture of the motors on a large scale. But great difficulties had still to be overcome. My system was based on the use of low frequency currents and the Westinghouse experts had adopted 133 cycles with the ob-

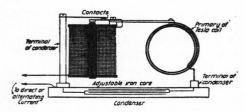

Fig. 3—Scheme of Circuit Connections In Tesla's Oscillation Transformer Shown in Fig. 1. The Secondary Circuit Which Slips Into the Primary Is Omitted.

ject of securing advantages in the transformation. They did not want to depart from their standard forms of apparatus and my efforts had to be concentrated upon adapting the motor to these conditions. Another necessity was to produce a motor capable of running efficiently at this frequency on two wires which was not easy of accomplishment. At the close of 1889, however, my services in Pittsburgh being no longer essential, I returned to New York and resumed experimental work in a laboratory on Grand Street, where I began immediately the design of high frequency machines. The problems of construction in this unexplored field were novel and quite peculiar and I encountered many difficulties. I rejected the inductor type, fearing that it might not yield perfect sine waves which were so important to resonant action. Had it not been for this I could have saved myself a great deal of labor. Another discouraging feature of the high frequency alternator seemed to be the inconstancy of speed which threatened to impose serious limitations to its use. I had already noted in my demonstrations before the American Institution of Electrical Engineers that several times the tune was lost, necessitating readjustment, and did not yet I foresee, what I discovered long afterwards, a means of operating a machine of this kind at a speed constant to such a degree as not to vary more than a small fraction of one revolution between the extremes of load.

The Invention of the Tesla Coil

From many other considerations it appeared desirable to invent a simpler device for the production of electric oscillations. In 1856 Lord Kelvin had exposed the theory of the condenser discharge, but no practical application of that important knowledge was made. I saw the possibilities and undertook the development of induction apparatus on this principle. My progress was so rapid as to enable me to exhibit at my lecture in 1891 a coil giving sparks of *five inches.* On that occasion I frankly told the engineers of a defect involved in the transformation by the new method, namely, the loss in the spark gap. Subsequent investigation showed that no matter what medium is employed be it air, hydrogen, mercury vapor, oil or a stream of electrons, the efficiency is the same. It is a law very much like that governing the conversion of mechanical energy. We may drop a weight from a certain height vertically down or carry it to the lower level along any devious path, it is immaterial insofar as the amount of work is concerned. Fortunately however, this drawback is not fatal as by proper proportioning of the resonant circuits an *efficiency of 85 per cent* is attainable. Since my early announcement of the invention it has come into universal use and wrought a revolution in many departments. But a still greater future awaits it. When in 1900 I obtained powerful discharges of 100 feet and flashed a current around the globe, I was reminded of the first tiny spark I observed in my Grand Street laboratory and was thrilled by sensations akin to those I felt when I discovered the *rotating magnetic field.*

The Thought Recorder

by Hugo Gernsback
with comments by N. Tesla & Others

Electrical Experimenter, May 1919

When the writer first conceived the idea of the thought recorder, he asked three prominent scientists regarding their views on recording thoughts electrically. The letters are reproduced herewith excerpted. It will be noted that Nikola Tesla disagrees with the writer as to thought transmission at all, but his letter nevertheless will give considerable food for thought to many readers. Dr. Lee de Forest, inventor of the audion, is not too sure about thought transmission. Dr. Greenleaf Whittier Pickard, the inventor of the silicon and pericon detector, as well as many other wireless specialties, has several interesting ideas, and his letter will certainly prove a revelation, particularly to those interested in radio.

Three Famous Scientists' Views On Thought Transmission

Although I am clinging to ideals, my conception of the universe is, I fear, grossly materialistic. As stated in some of my published articles, I have satisfied myself thoroughly through careful observation carried on for many years that we are simply automata acting in obedience to external influences without power or initiative. The brain is not an accumulator as commonly held in philosophy, and contains no records whatever of a phonographic or photographic kind. In other words, there is no stored knowledge or memory as usually conceived, our minds are blanks. The brain has merely the quality to respond, becoming more and more susceptible as the impressions are often repeated, this resulting in memory.

There is a possibility, however, which I have indicated years ago, that we may finally succeed in not only reading thoughts accurately, but reproducing faithfully every mental image. It can be done thru the analysis of the retina, which is instrumental in conveying impressions to the nerve centers and, in my opinion, is also capable of serving as an indicator of the mental processes taking place within. Evidently, when an object is seen, consciousness of the external form can only be due to the fact that those cones and rods of the retina which are covered by the image are affected differently from the rest, and it is a speculation not too hazardous to assume that visual-

ization is accompanied by a reflex action on the retina which might be detected by suitable instruments. In this way it might also be possible to project the reflex image on a screen, and with further refinement resorting to the principle involved in moving pictures, the continuous play of thoughts might be rendered visible, recorded and at will reproduced.

NIKOLA TESLA

Your article should be an interesting one, particularly as to the audion suggestion. The audion, however, seems to have a certain wavelength limitation, so that unless the waves to be recorded lie between about 3 x 10¹⁰ cm. and 3 x 10² cm., they are not apt to be "picked up." A mere likely range to search would be from: 3 x 10² cm. down to 3 x 10¹⁰ cm., that is, down to the harder Gamma rays, or to even shorter wavelengths, starting with the shorter Hertzian waves. Here the audion would be useless, save as a second stage in the detection, i.e., as an amplifier for some other form of detector.

GREENLEAF W. PICKARD

While I have little doubt that there is such a thing in nature as transference of thought from one brain to another, I am not aware that sufficient data has ever been gathered on such a highly abstruse subject to permit forming any definite opinion.

LEE DE FOREST

In studying the evolution of the human specie we must go back to the time when man proper, as we know him, had not as yet arrived on this planet. Our great biologists have irrefutable evidence that everything in Nature works, on a slow, laborious plan, one specie being developed slowly into another from the smallest animalculæ up to present man. When man was still in the what we may call animal stage, i.e., when he was not "thinking," as that term is understood, he was wholly guided by instinct. His "thoughts," if so they may be called, were probably on a much lower plane than thoughts of the average dog. The chances are that the present day dog probably "thinks" much better than prehistoric man. We also find that thought and language go hand in hand. Crudely speaking, prehistoric man had no better language than any highly developed animal, such as a dog, cat or a horse.

Through thousands of years of evolution, however, instinct developed into crude thought, and finally there came a time when prehistoric man really began to think, as we know the term. That was the time when he began to utter his thoughts by means of his voice. At first only a few crude words were formulated, and probably consisted of not much more than the gibberish of a chimpanzee. Little by little organized thought arrived, and words, translated into speech kept pace with the advancing thought of man. As the human race kept advancing at a slow pace, its thinking qualities increased little by little, and the senses correspondingly became more sharpened.

This is especially true of the human thinking machinery which perhaps has advanced more rapidly than the senses. Thus we find that certain senses have even been retarded, such as, for instance, sight, smell and hearing. When man lived his wild life it was very necessary for these senses to be much sharper than they are at present; hence our poor hearing, bad sight and very much poorer smell. On the other hand, as the battle for existence becomes more and more acute, and as moreover the battle is not as much physical as mental, it follows that the mind and its thinking machinery should naturally become more and more developed, which, in fact, it does. We may safely say that within the next hundred thousand years which is only a small span of time in man's evolution the human mind will be an entirely different sort of apparatus than it is today. Man's mental power will be infinitely greater than what it is at present. Already we have indications that man's thoughts, or the effects therefrom, do not necessarily have to remain within his skull, but that they actually radiate from the latter in a very imperfect manner. As the human race advances, there is no doubt that thought transference proper will become an accomplished fact. It has already been shown experimentally by Di Brazza, as well as Charpentier, that concentrated thinking will produce certain external effects, as for instance, a slight fluorescence on a zinc sulfide screen, or a suitably excited X-ray screen. This would tend to prove that thoughts are of an electrical nature, having probably a very short wave length. As most electrical effects in space are dependent upon wave motion, it should not be surprising therefore that thoughts or active thinking should give use to wave motion as well.

This theory is greatly strengthened by the fact that it has been proven beyond doubt that active thinking necessitates an expendi-

The Thought Recorder is an Instrument Recording Thoughts Directly by Electrical Means, On a Moving Paper Tape. Our Illustration Shows What a Future Business Office Will Look Like When the Invention, Which as Yet Only Exists in the Imagination, Has Been Perfected. By Pushing the Button A, the Tape is Started and Stopt Automatically So That Only Thoughts That Are Wanted Are Recorded.

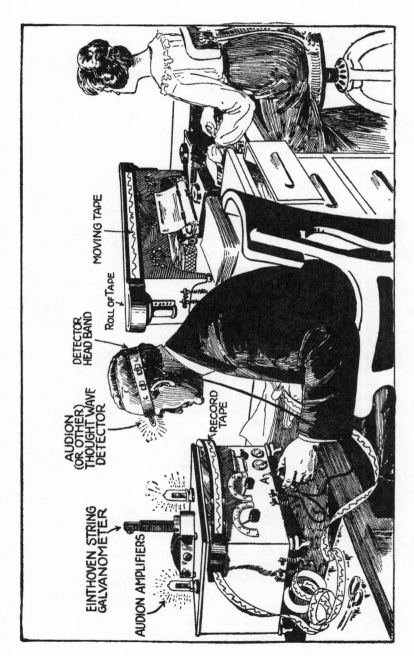

EINTHOVEN STRING
GALVANOMETER

AUDION AMPLIFIERS

AUDION
(OR OTHER)
THOUGHT WAVE
DETECTOR

DETECTOR
HEAD BAND

ROLL OF TAPE

MOVING TAPE

RECORD TAPE

ture of energy. If you sit perfectly quiet in a chair without expending any visible muscular energy, and if you concentrate very hard upon a certain problem, it is not infrequent that perspiration appears on your forehead from the .simple effort of thinking. Of course, this is rather a complex phenomenon, as the perspiration is not produced directly, but rather indirectly by the nerve centers working upon the human organs, principally the heart. Nevertheless, we know that thinking proper calls for an expenditure of energy in the brain itself. That this energy is considerable can also be shown experimentally.

It therefore cannot come as a surprise that the act of thinking should give rise to a direct wave motion, sending out from the brain certain waves in an analogous manner, to the spoken word which produces sound waves of a certain wave length. It is quite probable, however, that thought waves are simply another form of ether waves, the same as radio waves or light waves. Just as light rays traverse thru a thick glass pane without suffering any appreciable loss, just so will thought waves probably pass readily thru the human skull. If once we admit this theory it follows that it should be possible to detect such waves, and the only thing we need to know about them are the wave length and other important characteristics. We may take it for granted that the human brain, sensitive as it is, probably is not at all sensitive to these waves, and that by suitable apparatus it should become possible to detect such waves.

Just what apparatus are necessary to detect thought waves, or the effects there from, the writer does not venture to predict, but there is no doubt that the apparatus will be eventually found. Very little is known about the emission of the thought waves, and as a matter of fact the entire mechanism which produces thoughts is practically an unknown quantity, but every effect can be translated and recorded if once we understand its fundamentals.

Thus, fifty years ago the recordings of the voice would have appeared just as fantastic as the recording of thought appears today. People then rightly said, how could it be possible to hold the spoken word: it goes into the air and vanishes instantly. But once acoustics were better understood, it became a simple matter for the inventor of the phonograph to record the voice. Similarly, the day will come when thoughts will be recorded in an analogous manner. All that is necessary, as stated above, is suitable apparatus, and this should be easy to find.

The writer, in suggesting the audion as a thought-wave detector, does not do so because he thinks that it is suitable in all respects, or even feasible. His main idea is to set the stone rolling, and get other people to think about the problem, when sooner or later something surely will emerge. The writer has suggested the audion because it is known as one of the most sensitive electrical detecting apparatus for wave motion which we have today. If thoughts give rise to electrical waves, then by winding a few turns of wire on a headband and slipping it over the head, it should be possible to detect the presence of thought waves in the audion. On the other hand, too, the audion is enormously sensitive to capacity effects, as is well known. Thus, for instance, an oscillating audion is so sensitive that when the human hand is approached to it at a distance of even two feet, the presence of the hand will be heard plainly in the telephone receiver. If this is the case, the disturbance created in the mind should certainly make its presence felt in the audion, for thinking being first of a chemical nature, the act certainly must give rise to capacity effects. But let us assume that active thinking does not give rise to waves, electrical or otherwise, then the mere chemical action (and resulting capacity effects) should produce a disturbing influence upon the audion. These variations, if ever so slight, could then be amplified by the use of an audion or other amplifier, and the resultant effect be sent into an Einthoven string galvanometer. The small mirror attached to the string of the galvanometer will send its luminous pencil upon a light-sensitive paper tape which moves at a certain rate of speed in front of the mirror. The result will be a wavy line traced upon the paper tape in the well known manner. The paper tape traveling on will pass thru its fixing tank, and from there will emerge from the outside of the machine after it has past thru a small drying chamber heated by electrical coils.

From this, it will be understood that a man sitting in front of his Thought Recorder will be able to actually see on a tape his recorded thoughts, the same as the telegrapher working on a trans-Atlantic cable watches his tape and its wavy line produced by the Syphon recorder, emerging from the latter. Of course, it will be necessary for everyone to learn the "thought alphabet" just as the stenographer today must learn the various characters, or as the child is taught how to read and write, and as the cable operator must learn how to read the Syphon recorder "alphabet." All this, however, is simple, and is only an educational feature once the apparatus has been invented.

The objection naturally comes to the mind immediately that even if we have a machine to record the thoughts, all we will get on the tape will be a jumble of confused thoughts, and we might get a lot of things on the tape that were not meant for recording or registering at all. Such criticism, of course, is beyond controversy for the simple reason that when you write a letter by hand or on the typewriter, you have also at first a lot of confused thoughts, but you do not record such thoughts even by hand or by machine. It often happens after you have written down certain thoughts that you must change them.

The same is true of the thought recorder, of course.

Here the man who is doing the recording has a push button in his hand, shown at A in our illustration; if he does not press the button nothing is recorded. Once he wishes to record his thoughts in an orderly manner, he pushes the button and the tape begins moving simultaneously he will begin thinking in an orderly and slow manner the subject he wishes to record. He will think just as hard and just the same as if he were to pen down his thoughts by hand. The machine will then do the rest. If he thinks the wrong thoughts, naturally the wrong thoughts will be recorded, exactly the same as if he had written them by hand. There is no difference. In our illustration, our artist has endeavored to show that will happen in the future business office when the thought recorder comes into universal use. The business man of tomorrow will dictate his correspondence on the thought recorder, while his stenographer, who is perfectly familiar with his "thought writing," will type out the correspondence from the tape, which is kept moving by electric motors, in front of her eyes. A foot pedal stops or starts the motor, and there is also a reversing attachment so the tape will run backwards should she wish to re-read a certain portion of the tape.

The True Wireless
by Nikola Tesla
The Electrical Experimenter May 1919

In this remarkable and complete story of his discovery of the "True Wireless" and the principles upon which transmission and reception, even in the present day systems, are based, Dr. Nikola Tesla shows us that he is indeed the "Father of the Wireless." To him the Hertz wave theory is a delusion; it looks sound from certain angles, but the facts tend to prove that it is hollow and empty. He convinces us that the real Hertz waves are blotted out after they have traveled but a short distance from the sender. It follows, therefore, that the measured antenna current is no indication of the effect, because only a small part of it is effective at a distance. The limited activity of pure Hertz wave transmission and reception is here clearly explained, besides showing definitely that in spite of themselves, the radio engineers of today are employing the original Tesla tuned oscillatory system. He shows by examples with different forms of aerials that the signals picked up by the instruments must actually be induced by earth currents not etheric space waves. Tesla also disproves the "Heaviside layer" theory from his personal observations and tests. EDITOR.

Ever since the announcement of Maxwell's electro-magnetic theory scientific investigators all the world over had been bent on its experimental verification. They were convinced that it would be done, and lived in an atmosphere of eager expectancy, unusually favorable to the reception of any evidence to this end. No wonder then that the publication of Dr. Heinrich Hertz' results caused a thrill as had scarcely ever been experienced before. At that time I was in the midst of pressing work in connection with the commercial introduction of my system of power transmission, but, nevertheless, caught the fire of enthusiasm and fairly burned with desire to behold the miracle with my own eyes. Accordingly, as soon as I had freed myself of these imperative duties and resumed research work in my laboratory on Grand Street, New York, I began, parallel with high frequency alternators, the construction of several forms of apparatus with the object of exploring the field opened up by Dr. Hertz. Recognizing the limitations of the devices he had employed, I concentrated my attention on the production of a powerful induction coil but made no notable progress until a happy inspiration led me to the invention of the oscillation transformer. In the latter part of 1891 I was already so far advanced in the development of this new principle that I had at my disposal means vastly superior to those of the German physicist. All my previous efforts with Rhumkorf coils had left me unconvinced, and in order to settle my doubts I went over the whole ground once more, very carefully with these improved appliances. Similar phenomena were noted, greatly magnified in intensity, but they were susceptible of a different and more plausible explanation. I considered this to be so important that in 1892 I went to Bonn, Germany, to confer with Dr. Hertz in regard to my observations. He seemed disappointed to such a degree that I regretted my trip and parted from him sorrowfully. During the succeeding years I made numerous experiments with the same object, but the results were uniformly negative. In 1900, however, after I had evolved a wireless transmitter which enabled me to obtain electro-magnetic activities of many millions of horsepower, I made a last desperate attempt to prove that the disturbances emanating from the oscillator were ether vibrations akin to those of light, but met again with utter failure. For more than eighteen years I have been reading treatises, reports of scientific transactions, and articles on Hertz-wave telegraphy, to keep myself informed, but they have always impressed me like works of fiction.

The history of science shows that theories are perishable. With every new truth that is revealed we get a better understanding of Nature and our conceptions and views are modified. Dr. Hertz did not discover a new principle. He merely gave material support to a hypothesis which had been long ago formulated. It was a perfectly well-established fact that a circuit, a current, traversed by periodic emitted some kind of space waves, but we were in ignorance as to their character. He apparently gave an experimental proof that they were transversal vibrations in the ether. Most people look upon this as his great accomplishment. To my mind it seems that his immortal merit was not so much in this as in the focusing of the investigators' attention on the processes taking place in the ambient medium. The Hertz-wave theory, by its fascinating hold on the imagination, has stifled creative effort in the wireless art and retarded it for twenty-five years. But, on the other hand, it is impossible to over-estimate the beneficial effects of the powerful stimulus it has given in many directions.

As regards signaling without wires, the application of these radiations for the purpose was quite obvious. When Dr. Hertz was asked whether such a system would be of practical value, he did not think so, and he was correct in his forecast. The best that might have been expected was a method of communication similar to the heliographic and subject to the same or even greater limitations.

In the spring of 1891 I gave my demonstrations with a high frequency machine before the American Institute of Electrical Engineers at Columbia College, which laid the foundation to a new and far more promising departure. Although the laws of electrical resonance were well known at that time and my lamented friend, Dr. John Hopkinson, had even indicated their specific application to an alternator in the Proceedings of the Institute of Electrical Engineers, London, Nov. 13, 1889, nothing had been done towards the practical use of this knowledge and it is probable that those experiments of mine were the first public exhibition with resonant circuits, more particularly of high frequency. While the spontaneous success of my lecture was due to spectacular features, its chief import was in showing that all kinds of devices could be operated through a single wire without return. This was the initial step in the evolution of my wireless system. The idea presented itself to me that it might be possible, under observance of proper conditions of resonance, to transmit electric energy through the earth, thus dispensing with all artificial conductors. Anyone who might wish to examine impartially the merit of that early suggestion must not view it in the light of present day science. I only need to say that as late as 1893, when I had prepared an elaborate chapter on my wireless system, dwelling on its various

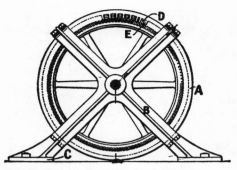

Alternator of 10,000 Cycles p.s. Capacity 10 K.W., Which Was Employed by Tesla in His First Demonstrations of High Frequency Phenomena Before the American Institute of Electrical Engineers at Columbia College, May 20, 1891. Fig. 1.

instrumentalities and future prospects, Mr. Joseph Wetzler and other friends of mine emphatically protested against its publication on the ground that such idle and far-fetched speculations would injure me in the opinion of conservative business men. So it came that only a small part of what I had intended to say was embodied in my address of that year before the Franklin Institute and National Electric Light Association under the chapter "On Electrical Resonance." This little salvage from the wreck has earned me the title of "Father of the Wireless" from many well-disposed fellow workers, rather than the invention of scores of appliances which have brought wireless transmission within the reach of every young amateur and which, in a time not distant, will lead to undertakings overshadowing in magnitude and importance all past achievements of the engineer.

The popular impression is that my wireless work was begun in 1893, but as a matter of fact I spent the two preceding years in investigations, employing forms of apparatus, some of which were almost like those of today. It was clear to me from the very start that the successful consummation could only be brought about by a number of radical improvements. Suitable high frequency generators and electrical oscillators had first to be produced. The energy of these had to be transformed in effective transmitters and collected at a distance in proper receivers. Such a system would be manifestly circumscribed in its usefulness if all extraneous interference were not prevented and exclusiveness secured. In time, however, I recognized that devices of this kind, to be most effective and efficient, should be designed **with due regard to the physical properties of this planet and the electrical conditions obtaining on the same.** I will briefly touch upon the salient advances as they were made in the gradual development of the system.

The high frequency alternator employed in my first demonstrations is illustrated in Fig. 1. It comprised a field ring, with 384 pole projections and a disc armature with coils wound in one single layer

High Frequency Alternator 12,000 cycles.

Adjustable condenser

Leads to lecture room

High tension secondary

Adjustable primary inductance

Diagram Illustrating the Circuit Connection and Tuning Devices Employed by Tesla in His Experimental Demonstrations Before the American Institute of Electrical Engineers With the High Frequency Alternator Shown in Fig. 1. Fig. 2.

which were connected in various ways according to requirements. It was an excellent machine for experimental purposes, furnishing sinusoidal currents of from 10,000 to 20,000 cycles per second. The output was comparatively large, due to the fact that as much as 30 amperes per square millimeter could be past through the coils without injury.

The diagram in Fig. 2 shows the circuit arrangements as used in my lecture. Resonant conditions were maintained by means of a condenser subdivided into small sections, the finer adjustments being effected by a movable iron core within an inductance coil. Loosely linked with the latter was a high tension secondary which was tuned to the primary.

The operation of devices through a single wire without return was puzzling at first because of its novelty, but can be readily explained by suitable analogs. For this purpose reference is made to Figs. 3 and 4.

In the former the low resistance electric conductors are represented by pipes of large section, the alternator by an oscillating piston and the filament of an incandescent lamp by a minute channel connecting the pipes. It will be clear from a glance at the diagram that very slight excursions of the piston would cause the fluid to rush with high velocity through

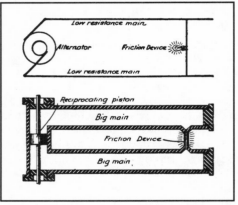

Electric Transmission Through Two Wires and Hydraulic Analog. Fig. 3.

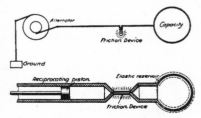

Electric Transmission Through a Single Wire Hydraulic Analog. Fig. 4.

the small channel and that virtually all the energy of movement would be transformed into heat by friction, similarly to that of the electric current in the lamp filament. The second diagram will now be self explanatory. Corresponding to the terminal capacity of the electric system an elastic reservoir is employed which dispenses with the necessity of a return pipe. As the piston oscillates the bag expands and contracts, and the fluid is made to surge through the restricted passage with great speed, this resulting in the generation of heat as in the incandescent lamp. Theoretically considered, the efficiency of conversion of energy should be the same in both cases.

Granted, then, that an economic system of power transmission through a single wire is practicable, the question arises how to collect the energy in the receivers. With this object attention is called to Fig. 5, in which a conductor is shown excited by an oscillator joined to it at one end. Evidently, as the periodic impulses pass through the wire, differences of potential will be created along the same as well as at right angles to it in the surrounding medium and either of these may be usefully applied. Thus at *a*, a circuit comprising an inductance and capacity is resonantly excited in the transverse, and at *b*, in the longitudinal sense. At *c*, energy is collected in a circuit parallel to the conductor but not in contact with it, and again at *d*, in a circuit which is partly sunk into the conductor and may be, or

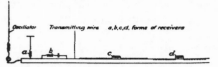

Illustrating Typical Arrangements for Collecting Energy in a System of Transmission Through a Single Wire. Fig. 5.

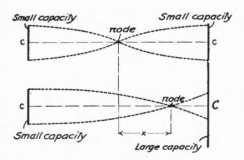

Diagram Elucidating Effect of Large Capacity on One End. Fig. 6.

not, electrically connected to the same. It is important to keep these typical dispositions in mind, for however the distant actions of the oscillator might be modified through the immense extent of the globe the principles involved are the same.

Consider now the effect of such a conductor of vast dimensions on a circuit exciting it. The upper diagram of Fig. 6 illustrates a familiar oscillating system comprising a straight rod of self-inductance $2L$ with small terminal capacities cc and a node in the center. In the

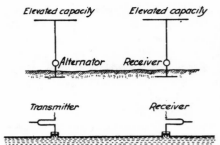

Transmission of Electrical Energy Through the Earth as Illustrated in Tesla's Lectures Before the Franklin Institute and Electric Light Association in February and March, 1893, and Mechanical Analog of the Same. Fig. 7.

lower diagram of the figure a large capacity *C* is attached to the rod at one end with the result of shifting the node to the right, through a distance corresponding to self-inductance *X*. As both parts, of the system on either side of the node vibrate at the same rate, we have

evidently, *(L + X) c = (L - X) C* from which $X = L \dfrac{C - c}{C + c}$.

When the capacity *C* becomes commensurate to that of the earth, *X* approximates *L*, in other words, the node is close to the ground connection. *The exact determination of its position is very important in the calculation of certain terrestrial electrical and devised geodetic data and I have special means with this purpose in view.*

My original plan of transmitting energy without wires is shown in the upper diagram of Fig. 7, while the lower one illustrates its mechanical analog, first published in my article in the *Century Magazine* of June, 1900. An alternator, preferably of high tension, has one of its terminals connected to the ground and the other to an elevated capacity and impresses its oscillations upon the earth. At a distant point a receiving circuit, likewise connected to ground and to an elevated capacity, collects some of the energy and actuates a suitable device. I suggested a multiplication of such units in order to intensify the effects, an idea which may yet prove valuable. In the analog two tuning forks are provided, one at the sending and the other at the receiving station, each having attached to its lower prong a piston fitting in a cylinder. The two cylinders communicate with a large elastic reservoir filled with an incompressible fluid. The vibra-

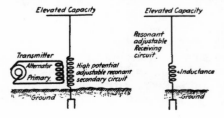

Tesla's System of Wireless Transmission Through the Earth as Actually Exposed in His Lectures Before the Franklin Institute and Electric Light Association in February and March, 1893. Fig. 8.

The Forerunner of the Audion - the Most Sensitive Wireless Detector Known, as Described by Tesla in His Lecture Before the Institution of Electrical Engineers, London, February, 1892. Fig. 9.

tions transmitted to either of the tuning forks excite them by resonance and, through electrical contacts or otherwise, bring about the desired result. This, I may say, was not a mere mechanical illustration, but a simple representation of my apparatus for submarine signaling, perfected by me in 1892, but not appreciated at that time, altho more efficient than the instruments now in use.

The electric diagram in Fig. 7, which was reproduced from my lecture, was meant only for the exposition of the principle. The arrangement, as I described it in detail, is shown in Fig. 8. In this case an alternator energizes the primary of a transformer, the high tension secondary of which is connected to the ground and an elevated capacity and tuned to the impressed oscillations. The receiving circuit consists of an inductance connected to the ground and to an elevated terminal without break and is resonantly responsive to the transmitted oscillations. A specific form of receiving device was not mentioned, but I had in mind to transform the received currents and thus make their volume and tension suitable for any purpose. This, in substance, is the system of today and I am not aware of a single authenticated instance of successful transmission at considerable distance by different instrumentalities. It might, perhaps, not be clear to those who have perused my first description of these improvements that, besides making known new and efficient types of apparatus, I gave to the world a wireless system of potentialities far beyond anything before conceived. I made explicit and repeated statements that I contemplated transmission, absolutely unlimited as to terrestrial distance and amount of energy. But, although I have overcome all obstacles which seemed in the beginning insurmountable and found elegant solutions of all the problems which confronted me, yet, even at this very day, the majority of experts are still blind to the possibilities which are within easy attainment.

My confidence that a signal could be easily flashed around the globe was strengthened through the discovery of the "rotating brush," a wonderful phenomenon which I have fully described in my address before the Institution of Electrical Engineers, London, in 1892, and which is illustrated in Fig. 9. This is undoubtedly the most delicate wireless detector known, but for a long time it was hard to pro-

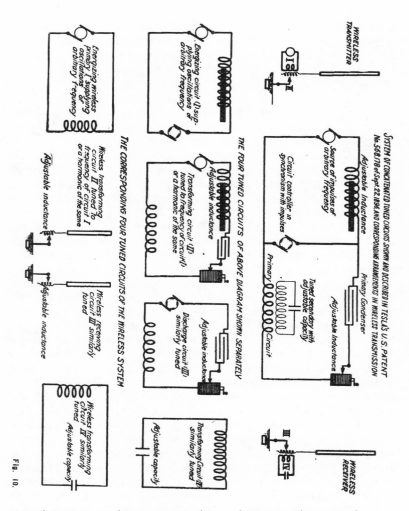

Tesla's System of Concatenated Tuned Circuits Shown and Described in U. S. Patent No. 568,178 of September 22, 1896, and Corresponding Arrangements in Wireless Transmission.

duce and to maintain in the sensitive state. These difficulties do not exist now and I am looking to valuable applications of this device, particularly in connection with the highspeed photographic method, which I suggested, in wireless, as well as in wire, transmission.

Possibly the most important advances during the following three or four years were my system of concatenated tuned circuits and methods of regulation, now universally adopted. The intimate bearing of these inventions on the development of the wireless art will appear from Fig. 10, which illustrates an arrangement described in my U.S. Patent No. 568178 of September 22, 1896, and corresponding dispositions of wireless apparatus. The captions of the individual diagrams are thought sufficiently explicit to dispense with further comment. I will merely remark that in this early record, in addition to indicating how any number of resonant circuits may be linked and regulated, I have shown the advantage of the proper timing of primary impulses and use of harmonics. In a farcical wireless suit in London, some engineers, reckless of their reputation, have claimed that my circuits were not at all attuned; in fact they asserted that I had looked upon resonance as a sort of wild and untamable beast! It will be of interest to compare my system as first described in a Belgian patent of 1897 with the Hertz-wave system of that period. The significant differences between them will be observed at a glance. The first enables us to transmit economically energy to any distance and is of inestimable value; the latter is capable of a radius of only a few miles and is worthless. In the first there are no spark-gaps and the actions are enormously magnified by resonance. In both transmitter and receiver the currents are transformed and rendered more effective and suitable for the operation of any desired device. Properly constructed, my system is safe against static and other interference and the amount of energy which may be transmitted is *billions of times greater* than with the Hertzian which has none of these virtues, has never been used successfully and of which no trace can be found at present.

A well-advertised expert gave out a statement in 1899 that my apparatus did not work and that it would take 200 years before a message would be flashed across the Atlantic and he even accepted stolidly my congratulations on a supposed great feat. But subsequent examination of the records showed that my devices were secretly used all the time and ever since I learned of this I have treated these Borgia-Medici methods with the contempt in which they are held by all fair-minded men. The wholesale appropriation of my inventions was, however, not always without a diverting side. As an example to the point I may mention my oscillation transformer operating with an air gap. This was in turn replaced by a carbon arc, quenched gap, an atmosphere of hydrogen, argon or helium, by a mechanical break with oppositely rotating members, a mercury interrupter or some kind of a vacuum bulb and by such *tours de force* as many new "systems" have been produced. I refer to this of course, without the slightest ill-feeling, let us advance by all means. But I cannot help thinking how much better it would have been if the ingenious men, who have originated these "systems," had invented something of their own instead of depending on me altogether.

Before 1900 two most valuable improvements were made. One of these was my individualized system with transmitters emitting a wave-complex and receivers comprising separate tuned elements cooperatively associated. The underlying principle can be explained in a few words. Suppose that there are n simple vibrations suitable for use in wireless transmission, the probability that any one tune will be struck by an extraneous disturbance is $\dfrac{1}{n}$. There will then remain $n-1$ vibrations and the chance that one of these will be excited is $\dfrac{1}{n-1}$, hence the probability that two tunes would be struck at the same time is $\dfrac{1}{n(n-1)}$. Similarly, for a combination of three the chance will be $\dfrac{1}{n(n-1)(n-2)}$ and so on. It will be readily seen that in this manner any desired degree of safety against the statics or other kind of disturbance can be attained provided the receiving apparatus is so designed that its operation is possible only through the joint action of all the tuned element. This was a difficult problem which I have successfully solved so that now *any desired number*

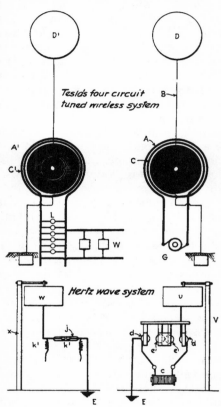

Tesla's four circuit tuned wireless system

Hertz wave system

Tesla's Four Circuit Tuned System Contrasted With the Contemporaneous Hertzwave System. Fig. 11.

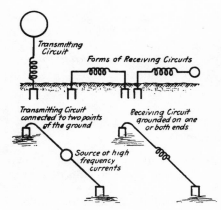

Arrangements of Directive Circuits Described in Tesla's U.S. Patent No. 613,809 of November 8, 1898, on "Method of and Apparatus for Controlling Mechanism of Moving Vessels or Vehicles." Fig. 12.

of simultaneous messages is practicable in the transmission through the earth as well as through artificial conductors.

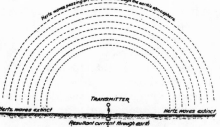

Diagram Exposing the Fallacy of the Gliding Wave Theory as Propounded in Wireless Text Books. Fig. 13.

The other invention, of still greater importance, is a peculiar oscillator enabling the transmission of energy without wires in any quantity that may ever be required for industrial use, to any distance, and with very high economy. It was the outcome of years of systematic study and investigation and wonders will be achieved by its means.

The prevailing misconception of the mechanism involved in the wireless transmission has been responsible for various unwarranted announcements which have misled the public and worked harm. By keeping steadily in mind that the transmission through the earth is in every respect identical to that through a straight wire, one will gain a clear understanding of the phenomena and will be able to judge correctly the merits of a new scheme. Without wishing to detract from the value of any plan that has been put forward I may say that they are devoid of novelty. So for instance in Fig. 12 arrangements of transmitting and receiving circuits are illustrated, which I have described in my U.S. Patent No. 613809 of November 8, 1898 on a Method of and Apparatus for Controlling Mechanism of Moving Vessels or Vehicles, and which have been recently dished up as orig-

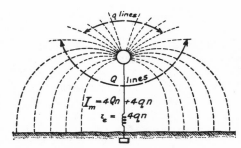

Fig. 14. Diagram Explaining the Relation Between the Effective and the Measured Current In the Antenna.

inal discoveries. In other patents and technical publications I have suggested conductors in the ground as one of the obvious modifications indicated in Fig. 5.

For the same reason the statics are still the bane of the wireless. There is about as much virtue in the remedies recently proposed as in hair restorers. *A small and compact apparatus has been produced which does away entirely with this trouble,* at least in plants suitably remodelled.

Nothing is more important in the present phase of development of the wireless art than to dispose of the dominating erroneous ideas. With this object I shall advance a few arguments based on my own observations *which prove that Hertz waves have little to do with the results obtained even at small distances.*

In Fig. 13 a transmitter is shown radiating space waves of considerable frequency. It is generally believed that these waves pass along the earth's surface and thus affect the receivers. I can hardly think of anything more improbable than this "gliding wave" theory and the conception of the "guided wireless" which are contrary to all laws of action and reaction. Why should these disturbances cling to a conductor where they are counteracted by induced currents, when they can propagate in all other directions unimpeded? The fact is that the radiations of the transmitter passing along the earth's surface are soon extinguished, the height of the inactive zone indicated in the diagram being some function of the wave length, the bulk of the waves traversing freely the atmosphere. Terrestrial phenomena which I have noted conclusively show that there is no *Heaviside layer,* or if it exists, it is of no effect. It certainly would be unfortunate if the human race were thus imprisoned and forever without power to reach out into the depths of space.

The actions at a distance cannot be proportionate to the height of the antenna and the current in the same. I shall endeavor to make this clear by reference to diagram in Fig. 14. The elevated terminal charged to a high potential induces an equal and opposite charge in the earth and there are thus Q lines giving an average current. $I=4Qn$

which circulates locally and is useless except that it adds to the momentum. A relatively small number of lines q however, go off to great distance and to these corresponds a mean current of $i_e = 4qn$ to which is due the action at a distance. The total average current in the antenna is thus $I_m = 4Qn+4qn$ and its intensity is no criterion for the performance. The q electric efficiency of the antenna is $\dfrac{q}{Q+q}$ and this is often a very small fraction.

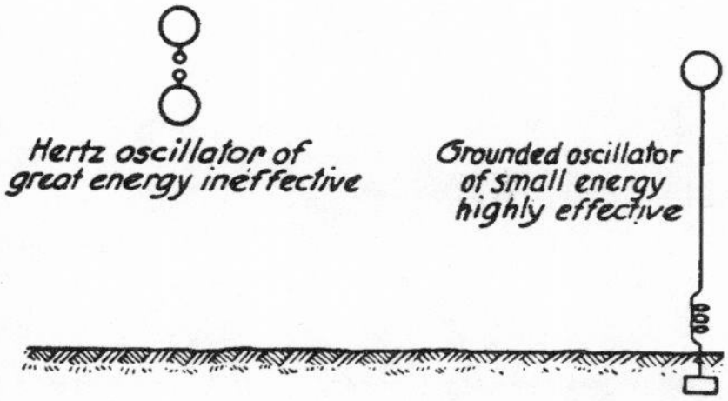

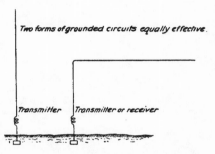

Fig. 15. Illustrating One of the General Evidences Against the Space Wave Transmission.

Fig. 16. Showing Unimportance of Relative Position of Transmitting and Receiving Antennae in Disproval of the Hertz-Wave Theory.

Dr. L. W. Austin and Mr. J. L. Hogan have made quantitative measurements which are valuable, but far from supporting the Hertz wave theory they are evidences in disproval of the same, as will be easily perceived by taking the above facts into consideration. Dr. Austin's researches are especially useful and instructive and I regret that I cannot agree with him on this subject. I do not think that if his receiver was affected by Hertz waves he could ever establish such relations as he has found, but he would be likely to reach these results if the Hertz waves were in a large part eliminated. At great distance the space waves and the current waves are of equal energy, the former being merely an accompanying manifestation of the latter in accordance with the fundamental teachings of Maxwell.

It occurs to me here to ask the question why have the Hertz waves been reduced from the original frequencies to those I have advocated for my system, when in so doing the activity of the transmitting apparatus has been reduced a billion fold? I can invite any expert to perform an experiment such as is illustrated in Fig. 15, which shows the classical Hertz oscillator and my grounded transmitting circuit. It is a fact which I have demonstrated that, although

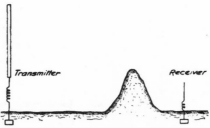

Fig. 17. *Illustrating Influence of Obstacle In the Path of Transmission as Evidence Against the Hertz-wave Theory.*

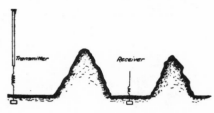

Fig. 18. *Showing Effect of Two Hills as Further Proof Against the Hertz-wave Theory.*

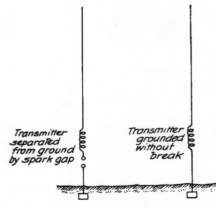

Fig. 19. *Comparing the Actions of Two Forms of Transmitter as Bearing Out the Fallacy of the Hertz-wave Theory.*

we may have in the Hertz oscillator an activity thousands of times greater, the effect on the receiver is not to be compared to that of the grounded circuit. This shows that in the *transmission from an airplane we are merely working through a condenser,* the capacity of which is a function of a logarithmic ratio between the length of the conductor and the distance from the ground. The receiver is affected in exactly the same manner as from an ordinary transmitter, the only difference being that there is a certain modification of the action which can be predetermined from the electrical constants. It is not at all difficult to maintain in communication between an airplane and a station on the ground, on the contrary, the feat is very easy.

To mention another experiment in support of my view, I may refer to Fig. 16 in which two grounded circuits are shown excited by oscillations of the Hertzian order. It will be found that the antennas can be put out of parallelism without noticeable change in the action on the receiver, this proves that it is due to currents propagated through the ground and not to space waves.

Particularly significant are the results obtained in cases illustrated in Figures 17 and 18. In the former an obstacle is shown in the path of the waves but unless the receiver is within the effective *electrostatic* influence of the mountain range, the signals are not appreciable weakened by the presence of the latter, because the currents pass under it and excite the circuit in the same way as if it were attached to an energized wire. If, as in Fig. 18, a second range happens to be beyond the receiver, it could only strengthen the

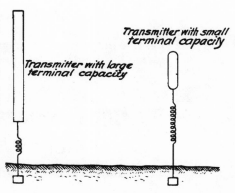

Fig. 20. Disproving the Hertz-wave Theory by Two Transmitters, One of Great and the Other of Small Energy.

Hertz wave effect by reflection, but as a matter of fact it detracts greatly from the intensity of the received impulses because the electric niveau between the mountains is raised, as I have explained in connection with my lightning protector in the EXPERIMENTER of February. Again in Fig. 19 two transmitting circuits, one grounded directly and the other through an air gap, are shown. It is a common observation that the former is far more effective, which could not be the case in a transmission with Hertz radiations. In like manner if two grounded circuits are observed from day to day the effect is found to increase greatly with the dampness of the ground, and for the same reason also the transmission through sea-water is more efficient.

An illuminating experiment is indicated in Fig. 20 in which two grounded transmitters are shown, one with a large and the other with a small terminal capacity. Suppose that the latter be 1/10 of the former but that it is charged to 10 times the potential and let the frequency of the two circuits and therefore the currents in both antennas be exactly the same. The circuit with the smaller capacity will then have 10 times the energy of the other but the effects on the receiver will be in no wise proportionate. The same conclusions will be reached by transmitting and receiving circuits with wires buried underground. In each case the actions carefully investigated will be found to be due to *earth currents*. Numerous other proofs might be cited which can be easily verified. So for example *oscillations of low frequency* are ever so much more effective in the transmission which is inconsistent with the prevailing idea. My observations in 1900 and the recent transmissions of signals to very great distances are another emphatic disproval.

The Hertz wave theory of wireless transmission may be kept up for a while, but I do not hesitate to say that in a short time it will be recognized as one of the most remarkable and inexplicable aberrations of the scientific mind which has ever been recorded in history.

The Home Treatment Of Tuberculosis By High Frequency Currents
by Dr. Frederick Finch Strong
Electrical Experimenter, Feb. 1918

Statistics show that one death in every seven is caused by tuberculosis, usually in the form called "Pulmonary tuberculosis," "Tuberculosis of the Lungs" or "Consumption." Sanitary regulations, isolation of cases and hygienic education are rapidly lowering this high death rate, but tuberculosis is still humanity's most terrible scourge. Throughout the ages "The Great White Plague" has done more to retard human progress than all the wars of the centuries not excepting the present Armageddon.

Fortunes have been spent in the study of the prevention and cure of this disease; countless fortunes have been made by quacks and mistaken enthusiasts who either claimed or believed themselves to have discovered "A Sure Cure for Consumption." The discovery of tuberculin by Koch was widely heralded as the longed-for panacea, but it proved a failure, and up to the present time no "specific" has been found for the cure of tuberculosis.

The importance of the subject is further emphasized when we reflect that even when it does not manifest as consumption, tuberculosis still does its insidious work in undermining the stamina of the entire race. Dr. A.C. Geyser states that "ninety per cent of all children are infected before their twelfth year, and nearly all bodies that come to autopsy show unmistakable signs of previously existing tubercular lesions." That more people do not develop the disease in its active form is due to the natural curative forces that are always at work in the human body.

Disease germs grow only in a suitable soil or medium; healthy human tissues do not furnish this medium. Only when these tissues are weak, inactive or charged with dead matter do they allow disease germs to multiply in their midst and produce their poisonous secretions.

In a previous article in the March, 1917, Experimenter "Electricity and Life" the writer called attention to the existence of the "Vital-force," or "Prana," through the activity of which all life is maintained. This is absorbed from the food, air and water, and is probably distributed by a circulating system all its own a subtle "Etheric Body" which interpenetrates the coarser molecules of the organism and is doubtless formed of imponderable chemical atoms finer than the gas atom and coarser than the electron. Just as modern physicists find it necessary to employ the hypothesis of "The Ether of Space" in order to account for the phenomena of radiant energy, so the most advanced of our physiologists and biologists are assuming the existence of the "Etheric Body" in order to explain the phenomena of life in animal and vegetable bodies.

Probably the great sympathetic nervous system distributes the life carrying matter of the etheric body in much the same way as the heart and blood vessels transmit food and oxygen to the cells and tissues. The latter circulation depends upon the maintenance of the former, for if pressure is made over certain nerve centers the blood stream is retarded or ceases altogether; pressure on another center stops the breathing mechanism and death from syncope follows. Great discoveries will be made in the immediate future through the study of the nerve currents and their relation to the Etheric Body and to "Vital Force."

It is because this vital circulation is fairly active in the majority of persons that so many recover spontaneously from pulmonary tuberculosis. But in cases of weak "vital resistance," where the Prana is not actively distributed to the lung cells, the tubercular germs grow, multiply, secrete poisons and ultimately make the physical body unfit for its human tenant who is forced to move elsewhere!

This lowered cell vitality results from hereditary weakness, improper food, and above all, from insufficient fresh air and out-of-door exercise. We can prevent this hereditary weakness in future generations by following Eugenic principles and exercising the same care that we now use in breeding blooded cattle and horses.

But meanwhile we have in our midst countless thousands of poor sufferers in whom tuberculosis exists in an active form, and the majority of whom face a lingering death scarcely less horrible than that resulting from the "poison gas" of the war zone. What can we do for these unfortunates? Those of them who can go to the special tuberculosis sanitariums and have daily treatment under proper surroundings stand a fair chance of recovery, especially when the disease is in the early stages. There are hundreds, however, who cannot go to such institutions.

When we do not use a machine it rusts and falls to pieces; when we do not use an organ or tissue of the human body the life-force and blood supply are diminished and we have a condition where disease germs can find a ready foothold. If certain parts of the lung are not periodically expanded by the inspired air they become "Anaemic", and susceptible to tubercular infection, which afterwards spreads to other parts of the lung. Now if we can find a way of revitalizing these anaemic areas, nature will use the blood and oxygen to start a regenerative process and the bacilli and dead cells will be thrown off in the expectoration. This latter material–the "tubercular"– sputum carries the infection to others; it should always be burned or received in vessels containing antiseptics such as creolin or sulphonaphthol. If this were always done the disease would soon be stamped out.

It is a well known fact that high-frequency currents when past through the body cause every molecule to vibrate to their particular periodicity, and this vibration produces secondary effects, notably the release of heat in the tissues and the increase of local blood supply. When an acute infection occurs in any part of the body for example, in acute bronchitis or "cold in the chest" we have as prominent symptoms fever, congestion, cough and expectoration. Most people think that by taking medicine to suppress these symptoms they can cure the disease; hence the use of cough-syrups, sedatives, etc. When the patient recovers under such treatment it is in *spite of the medicine rather than because of it,* for these symptoms are the very means nature is using to throw off the infection. Extra vital force is being wisely directed to the endangered area–hence the fever, heat, congestion and expectoration. Medical science has been working at the problem of "cure" from the wrong end. Instead of suppressing symptoms we must aid nature to throw off the disease-producing germs and neutralize their poisons. In other words we must assist and promote the process of inflammation. It is because the inflammation is not sufficiently vigorous that many cases of tuberculosis do not recover. The infected areas are usually anaemic to start with and after the infection becomes well established the general blood pressure drops and it is still more difficult to establish the healing inflammatory phenomena. Other germs come in and cause secondary infections which greatly hasten the progress of the disease.

Now the D'Arsonval High-frequency current, when applied to certain tissues of the body, produces all the effects of a natural inflammation–they cause "hyperaemia" or increase of blood to the parts, liberate heat and probably promote the circulation of the vital currents. This method is known as "diathermy" or "thermo-penetration" and has been successfully employed in many hospitals and clinics in treating pulmonary tuberculosis. Dr. Albert Geyser, of New York City, reports over *sixty per cent of recoveries* in cases so treated at his Clinic at Fordham University; others have reported equally good results, yet it is a fact that the State Boards of Health, the Public Sanatoriums and thousands of lung specialists ignore this important method of combatting the "Great White Plague."

For those who can make or procure a High-frequency apparatus, such as the writer described in the December, 1917, issue of the Electrical Experimenter or any other standard therapeutic high frequency apparatus giving both Tesla and D'Arsonval currents, the successful home treatment of tuberculosis is easily possible. The technique is exceedingly simple once daily for twenty-five minutes, the patient is given a D'Arsonval treatment a block-tin electrode attached

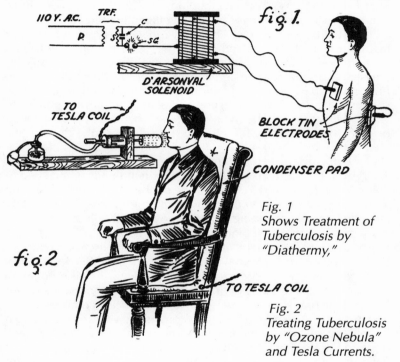

fig. 1

Fig. 1
Shows Treatment of Tuberculosis by "Diathermy,"

fig. 2

Fig. 2
Treating Tuberculosis by "Ozone Nebula" and Tesla Currents.

to a cord connected with each terminal of the solenoid being held or strapped in close contact with the skin of the patient's chest and the corresponding portion of the back (Fig. 1), so that the infected area of the lung lies in the path between the electrodes. The spark is opened until the patient feels a deep penetrating heat in the tissues between the tin electrodes. If the heat becomes uncomfortable the spark gap should be made shorter. All physicians' machines are provided with hot-wire milliamperemeters in the patient's circuit. When the meter is available the current strength can be adjusted so as to begin with 1,000 ma.,–gradually increasing this to 2,000 ma., by the second or third week of treatment. A home-made, machine operated from a one quarter K.W. wireless transformer will not give more than 1,200 ma., in Diathermy, but this can be made sufficient by increasing the length of the treatment to forty minutes. Continued daily for months this treatment will bring about recovery in a majority of consumptive patients. It is really necessary to add that proper dietary and hygienic measures should also be employed. Bulletins giving all needed information on these points can be had gratis from any State Board of Health. A physician should be consulted occasionally so that the progress of the case can be intelligently followed.

The use of the "Ozone Nebula" by *inhalation* is of great value in treating tubercular cases and when it is given in connection with Diathermy the chances of the patient's recovery are materially increased. A simple home-made apparatus for this treatment is made from a Welsbach lamp chimney mounted in a wooden upright as shown in the drawing (Fig. 2); one end of the chimney is open, from which the patient inhales the nebula; the other end is closed with a disc of wood through which is past a short glass tube three-eights inch in diameter; a brass rod 1/4" by 8" slides through a hole in the center of the disc. The inner end of the rod carries a small brass disc 1/16" by 1 1/2"; a small insulating rubber handle being attached to the outer end of he rod. A rubber tube connects the small glass tube with a *DeVilbis Oil Nebulizer* (procurable for a small sum at any large drug store) containing a small amount of 'Pinoleum"–a preparation containing oils of pine and eucalyptus.

In treating, the patient sits on the fiber condenser pad which is connected with one terminal of the Tesla coil; the other Tesla terminal is connected to the brass rod in the chimney which is brought up close to the patient's face until a fine purple effluve passes between him and the brass disc. An assistant now alternately compresses and releases the nebulizer bulb, thereby forcing the vaporized oil across the effluve so that it emerges from the open end of the chimney close to the nose and mouth of the patient. The patient, breathing naturally, inhales the chemical combination which is said to form between the oils and the ozone and nitrous vapors formed in the effluve; these are later released in the lung tissues. The action is antiseptic and also carries oxygen into the infected areas. Clinical tests seem to prove that there is a complicated vitalizing effect obtained by the simultaneous use of the ozone nebula and the Tesla currents.

This method was devised some years ago by the writer and differs from all the Ozone and "Oxylene" systems on the market in the above respect; in other words it is a combination treatment of two well recognized healing agents.

It should be given for only a few minutes at a time, and twice daily. If the vapor is too irritating, reduce the effluve by means of the spark gap or by withdrawing the sliding rod in the chimney.

No possible effects can follow the intelligent use of the electrotherapeutic methods above described, in the home treatment of tuberculosis, and the beneficial results are very marked.

Those interested in using high-frequency currents for the above purpose should obtain the back numbers of the Electrical Experimenter containing the articles "Electricity and Life," and "Treatment of Disease by High-frequency Currents" by the writer.

It is hoped that this article may be the means of enabling many sufferers from tuberculosis to regain their health.

After the disease is once cured its recurrence may be prevented by observing the following rules, which are equally appropriate for anyone who wishes to have more abundant health and life.

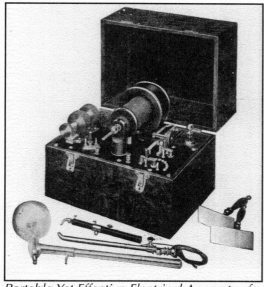

1. Breathe deeply plenty of fresh air, night and day.

2. Spend a part of each day walking or working out-of-doors.

3. Make at least one meal each day of nothing but fruit.

Portable Yet Effective Electrical Apparatus for

4. Make the rest of the diet largely wholly vegetarian.

Diathermy and Tesla Treatment of Tuberculosis.

5. Never "get sorry for yourself"; get busy and help the other fellow who is worse off than you are.